RON GOULART
writer

LEE SULLIVAN
artist

PAT BROSSEAU
letters

EVAN SKOLNICK
colorist

CARLOS LOPEZ
reprint editor

FABIAN NICIEZA
editor

CARL POTTS
executive editor

TOM DeFALCO
editor in chief

TEKWORLD™ Published by EPIC COMICS, 387 PARK AVENUE SOUTH, NEW YORK NY 10016. TEKWORLD (including all prominent characters featured in this issue and the distinctive likenesses thereof) is a trademark of William Shatner and is used only with permission. PRINTED IN THE U.S.A. First Printing: February 1994. ISBN #0-87135-985 GST #R127032852 10 9 8 7 6 5 4 3 2 1

Known to most as STAR TREK'S Captain Kirk, actor/director William Shatner now shifts his talents to a novel and now an upcoming television movie. TEK World is the story of ex-cop Jake Cardigan, who's framed for dealing an addictive brain stimulant called TEK, and sentenced to fifteen years of suspended animation. Now, mysteriously released after four years in the "Freezer", Cardigan is on the loose, and out for Justice!

CONTENTS

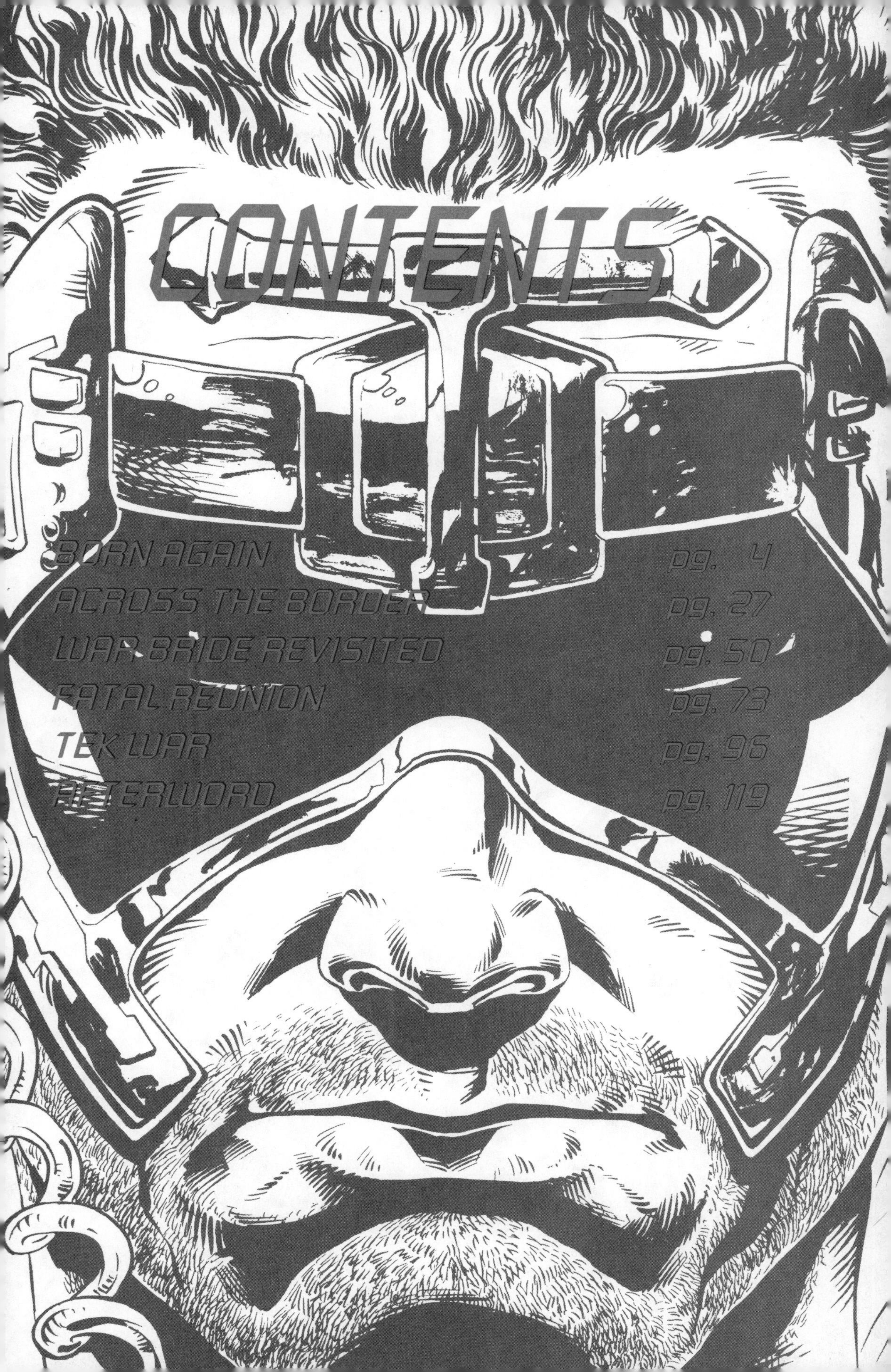

CHAPTER 1
BORN AGAIN

JAKE CARDIGAN DOESN'T KNOW HE'S GOING TO COME BACK TO **LIFE**.

UP IN THE ORBITING PENAL COLONY KNOWN AS **THE FREEZER** HE SLEEPS--UNAWARE OF ANYTHING.

TIME HAS PASSED, DAYS AND WEEKS AND THEN MONTHS AND YEARS, AND HE KEEPS SLEEPING THAT LONG SLEEP.

TODAY EVERYTHING IS GOING TO CHANGE, BUT JAKE DOESN'T KNOW ABOUT IT. NOT YET.

A HOT, HAZY MORNING IN THE LATE 21ST CENTURY. THE GREATER LOS ANGELES SPACE-PORT.
GLA SPACEPORT
I'M A BRAZIL WAR VET, SIR.
TAXI
PLEASE CAN YOU SPARE--
I'M IN A HURRY...
I'VE NO TIME FOR BEGGARS.
PRISON SHUTTLE TERMINAL
I'M WINGER. SOCAL PAROLE AUTHORITY. (M6) SCPS/31PB. HERE'S MY BOARD-ING PASS.
NICE MEETING YOU. WELCOME ABOARD.
WE'VE MET BEFORE, MISS... I OFTEN TAKE THIS SHUTTLE.
RIGHT... I SHOULD'VE REMEMBERED THE SUIT.
GLA

PARDON ME... HAVE *YOU* BEEN UP TO THE PRISON BEFORE?
MANY TIMES, MADAM. IN THE LINE OF DUTY.
MY HUSBAND WAS SENTENCED TO TEN YEARS. I'M GOING TO VISIT... WELL, JUST *LOOK* AT HIM.
THAT'S ALL I CAN DO... SINCE HE'LL BE IN SUSPENDED ANIMATION THE WHOLE TIME.
I ASSURE YOU IT'S VERY HUMANE. ALSO *ECONOMICAL*.
VISITORS GUIDE
POINTS TO REMEMBER
VISITORS GUIDE CRYOBIOTIC PENAL INSTITUT
IT SAYS HERE THAT WHEN HIS SENTENCE IS OVER, HE WON'T HAVE *AGED* AT ALL.
CAN THAT BE RIGHT?
PLEASE FASTEN SEATBELTS
YES, THAT'S WHAT SUSPENDED ANIMATION *MEANS*.
BUT *I'LL* BE TEN YEARS *OLDER*... AND I DON'T SEE HOW--
PENAL SHUTTLE · 4
PWS 4 'TIBERIUS'
DEAR LADY, SAVE THE *REST* OF YOUR QUESTIONS FOR THE *PRISON* ROBOTS.

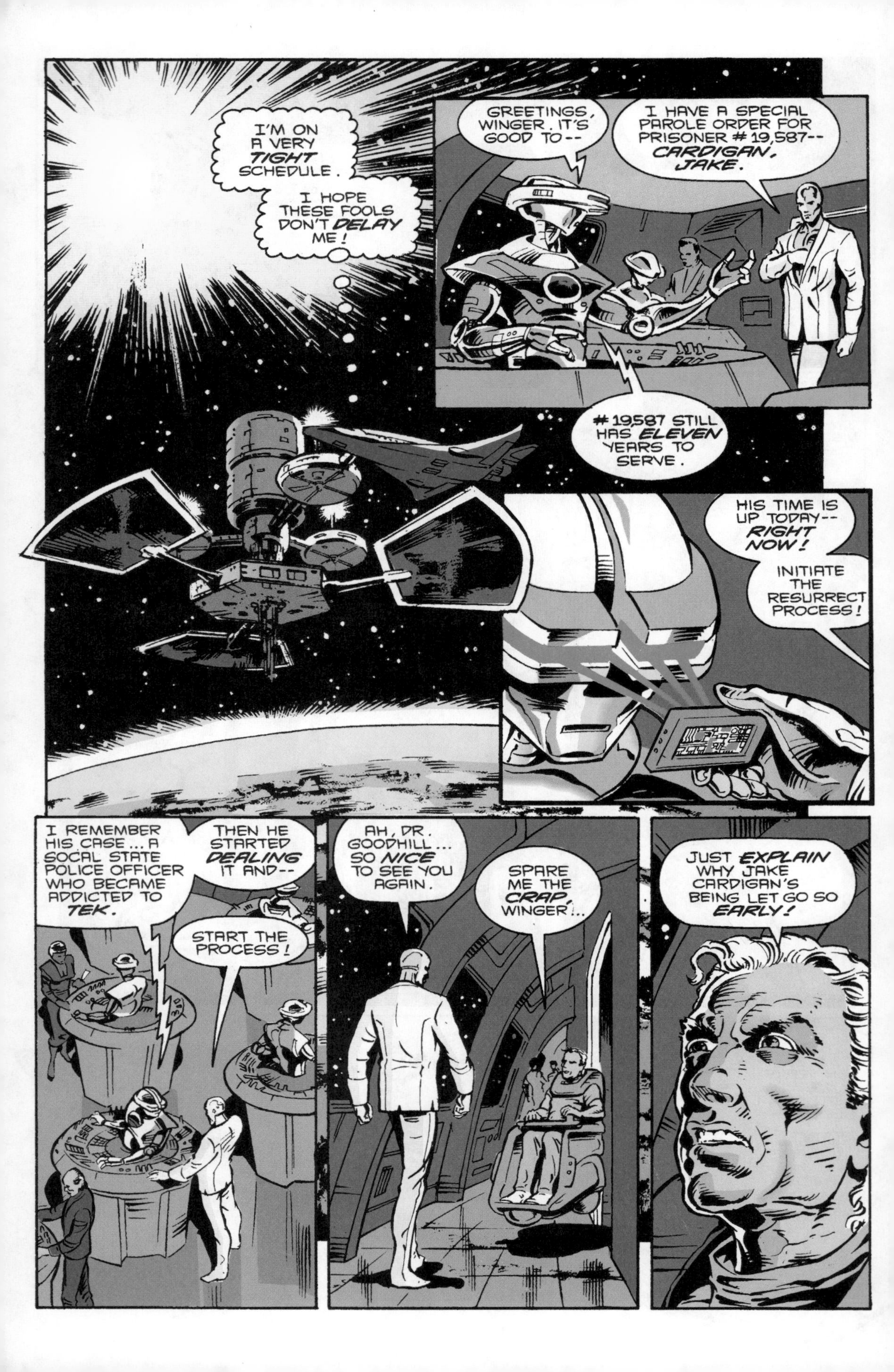
I'M ON A VERY TIGHT SCHEDULE.
I HOPE THESE FOOLS DON'T DELAY ME!
GREETINGS, WINGER. IT'S GOOD TO--
I HAVE A SPECIAL PAROLE ORDER FOR PRISONER #19,587-- CARDIGAN, JAKE.
#19,587 STILL HAS ELEVEN YEARS TO SERVE.
HIS TIME IS UP TODAY-- RIGHT NOW!
INITIATE THE RESURRECT PROCESS!
I REMEMBER HIS CASE... A SOCAL STATE POLICE OFFICER WHO BECAME ADDICTED TO TEK.
THEN HE STARTED DEALING IT AND--
START THE PROCESS!
AH, DR. GOODHILL... SO NICE TO SEE YOU AGAIN.
SPARE ME THE CRAP, WINGER!...
JUST EXPLAIN WHY JAKE CARDIGAN'S BEING LET GO SO EARLY!

HE'S BEEN GRANTED AN IMMEDIATE RELEASE.
THEN HE'S FINALLY BEEN CLEARED?
LET US SAY THAT CERTAIN INFLUENCE WAS USED TO GET HIM PAROLED.
YEAH, AND I KNOW HE WAS FRAMED FOUR YEARS AGO!
WAS "CERTAIN INFLUENCE" USED THEN, TOO?
AAGH--!
IT WOULD BE SUCH A PLEASURE TO CONTINUE OUR DISCUSSION LATER, DR. GOODHILL...
...BUT I'M IN A HURRY.
19587 CARDIGAN, JAKE
RESURRECTION LEVEL
REVIVE THIS PRISONER AS RAPIDLY AS POSSIBLE!

MOMENTS LATER...
I... FEEL... SORT OF... GROGGY...
WE HAVE A SHUTTLE TO CATCH. TRY TO SNAP OUT OF IT, CARDIGAN.
WINGER?
SO IT'S FIFTEEN YEARS *LATER*, HUH?
NO, ACTUALLY IT'S BEEN *JUST* FOUR.
ONLY FOUR? THEN THEY REALIZED I *WAS* INNOCENT!
YOU'VE BEEN GRANTED A *SPECIAL PAROLE*.
SOMEBODY INTERVENED? *WHO?*
I HAVE *NO* DATA ON THAT.

THEY'RE GIVING ME BACK MY LAZGUN, TOO?
YOUR PAROLE ALLOWS YOU TO CARRY WEAPONS.
STILL PRETTY UNSTEADY, EH, CARDIGAN?
DON'T WORRY-- I'M OKAY.
THEN GET MOVING, WILL YOU? WE'RE LATE.
SHUTTLE DOCK
REVIVAL AREA
IF YOU CAN'T WALK-- PERHAPS DR. GOODHILL WILL LOAN YOU HIS WHEEL-CHAIR.
DAMN YOU, WINGER!

C'MON, CARDIGAN-- USE THAT GUN ON ME!
THAT'LL GUARANTEE YOU FIFTY MORE YEARS HERE!
WARNING
WITH YOUR RECORD AS A TEK DEALER AND A CROOKED COP, YOU SHOULDN'T BE GETTING OUT AT ALL.
LOOK, I ADMITTED I USED TEK!
BUT I NEVER SOLD IT. NEVER BETRAYED ANYBODY.
ON SECOND THOUGHT, WINGER--YOU'RE NOT WORTH THE TROUBLE.
YOU'RE JUST A CHROME-PLATED COLLECTION OF NUTS AND BOLTS.

LATER, AT THE GLA SPACEPORT...
RRRT
RRRT
I'M OBLIGED TO GIVE YOU THIS.
IT'S A BRIEF REVIEW OF THE MAJOR CHANGES IN THE WORLD THAT TOOK PLACE WHILE YOU WERE ASLEEP.
GUESS I DO HAVE SOME CATCHING UP TO DO.
EXIT
GLA·SP
SECURITY
HMM. RAIN.
HERE'S SOMETHING ELSE YOU'LL NEED... A FORCE FIELD UMBRELLA.
I DON'T SEE MY WIFE AND SON ANYWHERE.
AREN'T THEY MEETING ME HERE?
OBVIOUSLY NOT. YOU'LL HAVE TO GET HOME ON YOUR OWN.
GOOD NIGHT, CARDIGAN-- I'LL MOST CERTAINLY STAY IN TOUCH.
SKYKABL
THIS ISN'T THE SORT OF HOMECOMING I WAS EXPECTING.
HEY-- TAXI!

THINGS LOOK DIFFERENT. GLA'S CHANGED.
BEEN AWAY FOR A WHILE, HUH?
FOR A WHILE, YEAH.
KATE?
DAN?
IT'S ME-- I'M HOME!
DAMN! WHERE ARE THEY?
WELCOME HOME! THIS IS YOUR RELIABLE HOUSEHOLD COMPUTER.
I'VE A RECORDED MESSAGE FROM YOUR FORMER WIFE.
FORMER WIFE?
WHAT THE HELL DO YOU MEAN?

HELLO, JAKE. WHEN I HEARD YOU WERE GETTING OUT, I TAPED THIS.
I... I WANTED TO LET YOU KNOW I DIVORCED YOU TWO YEARS AGO. THERE WAS NO WAY TO TELL YOU...UP THERE.
DIVORCED ME? BUT--

THE APARTMENT IS LEGALLY YOURS.
DANNY AND I ARE LIVING IN MEXICO NOW.
DANNY? YOU NEVER CALLED HIM THAT.
MY OLD BOSS, BENNETT SANDS, GOT ME A GREAT JOB HERE.

DANNY AND I ARE FINE--BUT WE DON'T WANT TO SEE YOU. NOT YET, ANY-WAY.
I'M SORRY, JAKE.
GOOD LUCK.

LATER THAT NIGHT...
CYBORG SLIM HAS CONTACTS WITH THE VIDPHONE COMPANY. MAYBE HE--
SLIM'S DEAD. YOU *WERE* AWAY A LONG TIME, HUH?
SORRY, JAKE--SO FAR I CAN'T FIND OUT A THING ABOUT WHERE YOUR MISSUS IS.
BUT, YOU USED TO BE ONE OF MY BEST INFORMANTS, *NEWS-BOY*.
OKAY, *YOU* KEEP TRYING.
YOU CAN COUNT ON ME.
AND, HEY, IT'S GOOD YOU'RE BACK, JAKE.
I WONDER--IS IT STILL WHERE I STASHED IT--?
ALL HERE...

BRAINBOX--HEADGEAR--TEK CHIPS.
NO! I *WON'T* GET STARTED AGAIN!

JAKE? WHERE ARE YOU?
HERE!
I'M HERE, KATE!
I REALIZED THE DIVORCE WAS A TERRIBLE MISTAKE.
IT WAS, YEAH.
I BELONG WITH YOU.
YOU DO.
I JUST COULDN'T STAY AWAY, DARLING.
NEITHER COULD I, DAD.
DAN--?

BUT AREN'T YOU FIFTEEN BY NOW?
OF COURSE-- DON'T I LOOK IT?
OH, YEAH. NOW YOU DO.
YOU DON'T SEEM GLAD WE CAME BACK.
SURE, I AM. IT'S JUST THAT...
WHAT'S WRONG, JAKE?
WHAT'S WRONG, DAD?
IT'S TIME TO LEAVE DREAM-LAND, AMIGO.
GOMEZ--? WHAT'RE YOU DOING HERE?
RIGHT NOW, JAKE, I'M FEELING LIKE A JERK FOR GETTING YOU DEFROSTED.

SINCE WE USED TO BE COPS TOGETHER, YOUR APARTMENT LET ME IN.
FORGIVE ME FOR INTRUDING ON YOUR HOMECOMING CELEBRATION.
SID-- KATE'S GONE-- I WAS UPSET.
BUT I'M NOT HOOKED ON TEK AGAIN!
YEAH, A LOT OF TEKHEADS SAY THAT.
LISTEN--I'M NOT A TEKHEAD AND NOT A DAMN DEALER, EITHER!
I DON'T NEED THIS STUFF!
TAKE IT EASY, AMIGO-- I STILL HAVE FAITH IN YOU.
THEN YOU MUST BE THE ONLY COP IN SOUTHERN CAL WHO DOES.
I'M NO LONGER A COP...
I'M A PRIVATE EYE NOW--AND I NEED A PARTNER AGAIN.

HOW COME YOU'RE NOT WITH THE SOCAL STATE POLICE?
OH, I KEPT TRYING TO PROVE YOU WERE FRAMED. THAT ANNOYED LOTS OF PEOPLE.
BUT I'M HAPPIER IN MY NEW JOB --RICHER, TOO.
I'M WITH THE COSMOS DETECTIVE AGENCY.
MY BOSS IS WALT BASCOM AND HE'S HONEST AND UPRIGHT-- MORE OR LESS...
SO IT WAS YOU AND THE COSMOS OUTFIT THAT GOT ME PAROLED?
TURNS OUT JUSTICE TAKES MONEY AND INFLUENCE.
I PERSUADED BASCOM TO USE PLENTY OF BOTH. HE GOT YOU OUT OF THE FREEZER SO HE COULD HIRE YOU.
WHAT SORT OF JOB DID YOU CONVINCE HIM HE NEEDS ME FOR?
THERE'S AN IMPORTANT CASE IN THE WORKS-- WE'LL TEAM UP ON IT.
WE HAVE TO FIND SOME-BODY-- DOWN IN MEXICO.
ZEROHOL

I'LL GIVE YOU SOME DETAILS.
BY THE WAY-- YOU WOULDN'T MIND ENCOUNTERING A FORMER LADYFRIEND, WOULD YOU?
LOADING DATA
DEPENDS ON WHICH ONE, SID.
WHOA NOW-- THAT'S WARBRIDE!
SI, IT IS. LADY'S BECOME A PRETTY POWERFUL REBEL LEADER. SHE CONTROLS A LARGE CHUNK OF MEXICO.
THIS CASE INVOLVES HER?
MAYBE-- AND I CONVINCED BASCOM YOU'RE ABSOLUTELY THE BEST HOMBRE FOR THE JOB.
MOSTLY BECAUSE OF YOUR OLD-- FRIENDSHIP-- WITH THE LADY.
WE WERE NEVER FRIENDS. WE JUST SLEPT TOGETHER. YEARS AGO.
IF YOU DON'T DO THIS FOR BASCOM, HE'LL BE SORRY HE PULLED STRINGS TO GET YOU OUT.
YOU MIGHT END UP BACK IN THE FREEZER.

I'LL TAKE THE JOB-- BE FUN WORKING TOGETHER AGAIN.
AND THREATS WEREN'T NECESSARY, SID.
THREATS WERE MY BOSS'S IDEA.
NEXT
SEQUENCE
OKAY, THIS IS DR. LEON KITTRIDGE. WELL-KNOWN ELECTRONICS EXPERT.
WORKED IN INDUSTRY-- TAUGHT AT COLLEGES HERE-ABOUTS.
"HERE'S HIS DAUGHTER, BETH. ALSO AN ELECTRONICS WHIZ.
"PRETTY, THOUGH A MITE ON THE SLIM SIDE. MORE YOUR TYPE, AMIGO.
"NEXT UP IS A SIMULATION. LAST WEEK THE DOC AND HIS SKINNY DAUGHTER TOOK OFF FOR A JAUNT INTO MEXICO.
"WHILE THEY WERE OVER THE GREAT FOREST, WHICH USED TO BE PART OF THE WORLDWIDE PROJECT TO CONTROL THE GREEN-HOUSE EFFECT...
"...THEIR SKY-CRUISER APPARENT-LY CRASHED."

THEIR INSURANCE COMPANY WANTS COSMOS TO FIND OUT WHETHER THE KITTRIDGES ARE DEAD OR ALIVE.
SO FAR, IT'S BEEN IMPOSSIBLE TO GET ANYONE SAFELY INTO WARBRIDE'S NECK OF THE WOODS.
WHICH IS WHERE WE COME IN, HUH?
SI, WITH YOUR CONTACTS AND MY CHARM-- WE CAN DO IT.
SOUNDS LIKE WE'RE A WINNING TEAM AGAIN.
MAYBE I'LL EVEN HAVE TIME IN MEXICO TO FIND OUT WHERE KATE IS.
THINK IT'D BE WISER TO STAY CLEAR OF HER.
WHAT ARE YOU GETTING AT, SID?
NOTHING. JUST IDLE CHATTER. SORRY.
I'LL PICK YOU UP AT 10 A.M. MAÑANA, JAKE.
WE HAVE AN IMPORTANT INFORMANT TO TALK TO BEFORE HEADING SOUTH.
SSHHH

NEXT MORNING...
SO WHO ARE WE MEETING, SID?
ONE DR. HILDA DANENBERG-- SHE USED TO BE A COLLEAGUE OF THE MISSING DR. KITTRIDGE.
AND A VERY CLOSE CHUM, SO I HEAR.
WE MEETING HER AT HOME?
NOPE, AT THE BOARDWALK IN THE MALIBU SECTOR.
SHE'S CONCERNED ABOUT HER SAFETY. PREFERS TO MEET IN SECRET.
THERE'S A VID OF THE LADY.
CLAIMS TO HAVE IMPORTANT INFO ABOUT THE DOC AND HIS DAUGHTER.
OCCURS TO ME, A BEACH-FRONT MALL ISN'T A VERY PRIVATE PLACE TO MEET.
NAVCOMP
GRID 210758
YOU'RE THINKING OF THE PLACE THE WAY IT USED TO BE, JAKE.
THESE DAYS IT'S NEVER CROWDED.

AIRSEA
WE'RE EARLY-- LET'S WALK AROUND, SID.
THE BOARDWALK REALLY HAS SLIPPED IN FOUR YEARS.
IT WAS A TEKKIE HANG-OUT COUPLE YEARS AGO.
LOT OF DAMAGE GOT DONE BEFORE THEY MOVED ON.
IS THE TEK PROBLEM WORSE IN GLA NOW?
USE IS UP TWENTY PERCENT-- BAD SIDE EFFECTS ARE INCREASING.
AND WITH A RELATIVELY NEW DRUG-- ESPECIALLY AN ELECTRONIC ONE-- YOU STILL GET SOME SCARY SURPRISES!
LONGTIME USERS ARE HAVING SEIZURES, FLASHBACKS AND SERIOUS FITS.
YOU REALLY OUGHT TO GIVE UP THE STUFF, AMIGO.
I TOLD YOU-- I QUIT!
BUT, DAMN IT, SID-- DON'T GO PREACHING TO ME!
IF I WANT A SERMON-- I'LL GO FIND WINGER!

SAY, THERE'S THE GOOD DOCTOR...
...AND THERE GOES THE PRIVACY I THOUGHT WE'D HAVE!
MAMA MIA's
PIZZERIA
I BETTER GO SHOO THE WALKER AWAY.
HEY-- FELLA-- DON'T ANNOY THE LADY!
LEAVE HER ALONE, HOMBRE!
BHWHOOUM!
NEXT:
ACROSS THE BORDER

CHAPTER 2
ACROSS THE BORDER

ACROSS THE BORDER
MAMA MIA'S PIZZERIA
JAKE CARDIGAN AND HIS PARTNER, SID GOMEZ, VISITED THE BOARDWALK IN THE MALIBU SECTOR OF GREATER LOS ANGELES TO MEET AN INFORMANT...
THE MEETING DIDN'T GO ESPECIALLY WELL.

SID!
HEY, THIS DOINK'S GOT SOME GOOD STUFF ON HIM! LOOK AT THE STUNGUN!
HERE'S A BANX CARD!
DROP THAT! GET AWAY FROM HIM!
YES, RIGHT AWAY, SIR.
WE WERE JUST BEING GOOD SAMARITANS, SIR.
SEND AN AMBULANCE TO THE BOARDWALK, QUICK!
I'VE GOT AN INJURED MAN HERE!

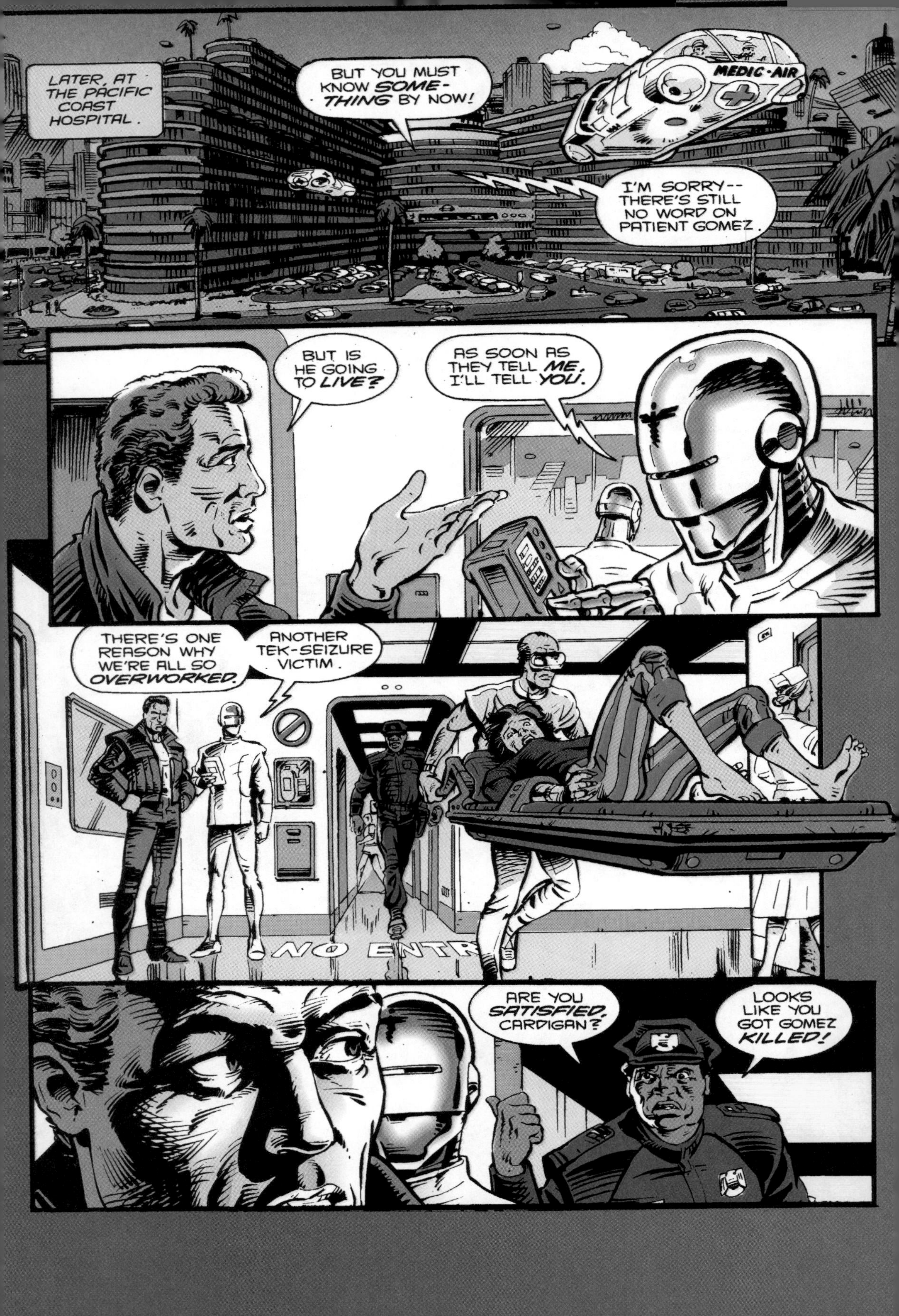
LATER, AT THE PACIFIC COAST HOSPITAL.
MEDIC-AIR
BUT YOU MUST KNOW SOMETHING BY NOW!
I'M SORRY-- THERE'S STILL NO WORD ON PATIENT GOMEZ.
BUT IS HE GOING TO LIVE?
AS SOON AS THEY TELL ME, I'LL TELL YOU.
THERE'S ONE REASON WHY WE'RE ALL SO OVERWORKED.
ANOTHER TEK-SEIZURE VICTIM.
NO ENTR
ARE YOU SATISFIED, CARDIGAN?
LOOKS LIKE YOU GOT GOMEZ KILLED!

WHAT CAUSED THE EXPLOSION, CAPTAIN HAMBRICK?
TURNS OUT THE BEGGAR WAS AN ANDROID-- LOADED WITH EXPLOSIVES!
"THEY CALL 'EM KAMIKAZES.
"IT'S SOMETHING YOUR TEKLORD BUDDIES COOKED UP WHILE YOU WERE ON ICE. THEY USE 'EM FOR ASSASSINATIONS AND THE LIKE.
"TELL YOU SOMETHING ELSE, CARDIGAN-- THE LADY WHO GOT BLOWN UP WAS AN ANDROID, TOO."
THEN WHERE'S THE REAL DR. DANEN-BERG?
THAT'S WHAT WE'D LIKE TO KNOW. WE WANT TO TALK TO HER.

PATIENT GOMEZ IS NOT IN SERIOUS CONDITION. YOU CAN SEE HIM NOW.
GREAT!
WAIT! I'LL QUESTION HIM FIRST.
HE'LL PROBABLY PREFER AN HONEST COP TO TALK TO RIGHT NOW.
YOU'RE NOT MY BOSS ANYMORE, HAMBRICK! SO QUIT--
C'MON, HIT ME! THAT'LL FIX YOUR PAROLE REAL GOOD.
FINE, GO AHEAD AND TALK TO SID.
I'M STILL GOING TO CLEAR UP THIS MESS BEFORE YOU DO.
AND I'LL PROVE I WAS FRAMED FOUR YEARS AGO!

LATER, AT THE COSMOS DETECTIVE AGENCY IN THE LAGUNA SECTOR OF GREATER L.A...
TENDOWN CORP.
JONATHAN CARDIGAN JR., FORMER SOCAL STATE POLICE OFFICER, ALSO SERVED ON BORDERLAND PATROL. RECENTLY PAROLED FROM ORBITING PENAL COLONY SERVING FOUR YEARS OF A FIFTEEN-YEAR SENTENCE FOR DEALING IN TEK. SUBJECT CLAIMED THAT HE WAS FRAMED.
COSMOS
QUITE A CAREER, CARDIGAN.
LET'S SEE--DISHONEST, SNEAKY, INSUBORDINATE, SARCASTIC, IRREVERENT, UNPATRIOTIC... ANYTHING ELSE?
LISTEN--HAMBRICK ALREADY GAVE ME A LECTURE!
IF YOU THINK I'M A CROOK, DON'T HIRE ME, BASCOM!
RELAX. I TRUST GOMEZ, AND HE SAYS YOU'RE TRUE BLUE.
BESIDES, I NEED A FEISTY, INSUBORDINATE OPERATIVE--ESPECIALLY ONE WHO KNOWS HIS WAY AROUND MEXICO.

THERE'S SOMETHING ABOUT THIS DISAPPEAR-ANCE YOU DON'T KNOW YET.
DR. KITTRIDGE AND HIS DAUGHTER BETH HAVE JUST ABOUT PERFECTED AN ANTI-TEK SYSTEM.
THAT DOES CHANGE THINGS.
MAKES THIS MORE THAN A SIMPLE INSURANCE CASE.

YEP, IT COULD BE THAT SOME MAJOR TEK CARTELS ARE INVOLVED IN WHAT-EVER'S HAPPENED TO THEM.

THE TEKLORDS MAY HAVE KILLED THE KITTRIDGES, KIDNAPPED THEM...
...OR BE COMPETING WITH YOU TO FIND THEM.

THIS IS BENNETT SANDS, THE LAD THE KITTRIDGES WERE ON THEIR WAY TO SEE WHEN THEY DISAPPEARED.
I KNOW SANDS. MY WIFE--EX-WIFE--USED TO WORK FOR HIM.
MY ONLY ADVICE IS--DON'T TRUST HIM.

GOMEZ FIGURES SHE MAY BE NICER TO YOU.
LET'S HOPE SO.
I WANT TO HIT THE BORDER-LAND SECTOR FIRST-- LOOK UP SOME OLD CON-TACTS AND THEN ARRANGE FOR SAFE CONDUCT INTO HER DOMAIN.
HERE'S THE REBEL LADY WHO CONTROLS THE PART OF MEXICO WHERE THE MISSING PAIR DISAPPEARED.
YEAH-- WARBRIDE.
TWO OTHER COSMOS OPS HAVE COME TO GRIEF TRYING TO GET INTO THE GREAT FOREST AREA.
THING IS-- I DON'T THINK I CAN WAIT UNTIL SID IS UP AND AROUND.
DAMNED RIGHT YOU CAN'T. YOU LEAVE TONIGHT!

COSMOS DETECTIVE AGENCY TOWER 2
I BETTER GET HOME AND PACK.
HEY, TAXI!
TAXI
TAKE ME TO THE PASADENA SECTOR.
TAXI
FSSSHH
WHOA NOW-- YOU'RE FLYING IN THE WRONG DIRECTION!
WE'RE TAKING A LITTLE SIDE TRIP, CARDIGAN.

I DON'T THINK SO!
THOK
CRRK
I'LL PILOT THIS CRATE MYSELF...
CAUTION, MR. CARDIGAN. ANY TAMPERING WITH THE CONTROLS MAY PROVE FATAL!
SPACELAND
BESIDES, WE HAVE ARRIVED AT OUR DESTINATION.
MARS
TAXI
THE CENTRIFU
LUNAR MODULE
YOU'LL FIND AN OLD FRIEND WAITING AT THE MOON RIDE.

WELCOME BACK FROM PRISON, MY BOY. COME ABOARD.
WINTERGUILD--?

MATTER OF FACT, NOW IT'S INTERNATIONAL DRUG CONTROL AGENCY DIRECTOR CURT WINTERGUILD, AT YOUR SERVICE.
YEAH, GREAT. YOU'RE ALSO BLURRED AROUND THE EDGES, "CURT". BETTER TUNE YOUR HOLOGRAM RE-MOTE PROJECTOR.

I'M ACTUALLY IN MEXICO JUST NOW, CARDIGAN.
WORKING ON THE KITTRIDGE CASE?

YES--AND I HEAR COSMOS HAS PUT YOU ON IT.
I'M WARNING YOU--QUIT RIGHT NOW!

OUR AGENCY IS CLOSE TO LINKING YOUR OLD TEK-LORD CRONY, SONNY HOKORI, TO THIS CASE.
WE MAY ALSO BE ABLE TO PROVE THAT BENNETT SANDS LURED THE KITTRIDGES INTO A TRAP.
WE DON'T WANT YOU NOSING AROUND!

IF YOU INTERFERE-- YOU COULD END UP BACK IN THE FREEZER!
AND KEEP IN MIND, MY BOY-- THERE ARE EVEN WORSE THINGS THAN PRISON.

YOU KEEP IN MIND THAT I'M GOING TO MEXICO--
--AND WHEN WE MEET FACE-TO-FACE-- WATCH OUT!

...SO AS IT TURNS OUT, SID, THERE'S A TEK ANGLE TO THIS CASE.
OCCURS TO ME, AMIGO, THAT THE KITTRIDGES MAYBE AREN'T DEAD.
THEY MIGHT'VE FAKED THAT CRASH--MAYBE THROW OFF THE TEK KING-PINS?
TURNS OUT SONNY HOKORI IS ONE OF THOSE KING-PINS.
I'D LIKE TO MEET SONNY AGAIN...
I KNOW YOU THINK HE FRAMED YOU, JAKE--
--BUT WATCH IT--REVENGE CAN BE TRICKY.
YEAH, I'LL KEEP THAT IN MIND.
SELECT :-
VISION ONE TWO WAY
SOUND ONLY
1 2 3 4 5
6 7 8 9 0
BEEN A LONG TIME SINCE I'VE BEEN ACROSS THE BORDER.

THAT NIGHT...
TAXI
ROOSTER
FIGHT NITE
Tonight
PACO'S POKER PALACE
BREAK FOR THE BORDER POOL
MAMA LAVIDA'S Natural BORDELLO
Hotel BORDERLAND
WELCOME TO THE HOTEL BORDERLAND, SEÑOR.
BY THE WAY--I'M A NEW MODEL BELLBOT.
FROM YOUR TOURIST POINT OF VIEW--
--AM I PICTURESQUE AND COLORFUL ENOUGH?
MORE THAN ENOUGH.
WELL, THIS TOWN HASN'T CHANGED MUCH... IT'S AS SLEAZY AS EVER.
CLUMP
WHAT THE DEVIL WAS THAT?
BRAKK!

BRZZZZZZ
KSSHH

HERE! I DON'T WANT THIS DAMN THING!
BUT I DO WANT TO TALK TO YOU!
GOT TO FIND OUT WHO HIRED THIS GOON--
HALT AT ONCE!
YOU WILL COME WITH US, SEÑOR.

I'M SORRY MY MEN WERE SOMEWHAT ROUGH, JAKE.
WHEN I HEARD MY OLD AMIGO WAS IN TOWN, I TOLD THEM MERELY TO INVITE YOU HERE.
I WAS GOING TO COME HERE ANYWAY, ERNEST.
WHAT I NEED IS ADVICE ON HOW TO TRAVEL SAFELY INTO THE GREAT FOREST AREA.
CAPT. E. MANZANO
AH, YES -- YOU'RE A PRIVATE DETECTIVE NOW, AREN'T YOU?
POLIC
YEAH, FOR COSMOS. WE'VE BEEN HIRED TO FIND DR. KITTRIDGE AND HIS DAUGHTER.
AS YOU KNOW, WARBRIDE'S REBEL ARMY CONTROLS THAT ENTIRE SECTOR.
"HER SECOND-IN-COMMAND IS RAFE VARGAS, A RUTHLESS AND VIOLENT MAN."
VARGAS IS ALSO HER LOVER-- AND A VERY JEALOUS MAN.
HEY, I DON'T WANT TO SLEEP WITH HER --
-- JUST GET TO THE CRASH SITE WITHOUT BEING KILLED.

"OKAY, JAKE... YOUR BEST BET IS TO GO TO THE CITY OF CHIHUAHUA. THAT'LL PUT YOU CLOSE TO REBEL TERRITORY.
"A HOODLUM THERE NAMED GLOBO HAS CONTACTS WITH WAR-BRIDE'S PEOPLE -- BUT HE'S NOT EN-TIRELY TRUSTWORTHY.
"AN OLD FRIEND OF YOURS, CARLOS RIBERA, IS NOW A GENERAL IN HER ARMY. IF YOU CAN CONTACT HIM, HE'LL HELP.
"HOLD ON A SEC-- YOU'VE GOT AN EMERGENCY CALL COMING IN, JAKE."

BASCOM.
WE JUST HEARD FROM THE ELUSIVE DR. DANENBERG.
SHE'S DOWN THERE IN MEXICO --AND MOST ANXIOUS TO TALK TO YOU.

WHERE EXACTLY IS SHE?
A TOWN CALLED CASAS GRANDES-- ABOUT 150 MILES SOUTH OF YOU.
MEET HER AT SEÑOR BLUE'S CAFE AT EIGHT TONIGHT.

AND BE EXTRA CAREFUL, JAKE.
THAT LADY SEEMS TO ATTRACT EXPLO-SIONS.

MADE IT!
DIDN'T THINK THIS RENTED JALOPY HAD IT IN IT...

TOROS ELECTRICOS
THE NAME IS CARDIGAN.
BUENO. SEÑOR BLUE AWAITS YOU IN HIS OFFICE.

THROUGH HERE--YOU AND THE LADY WILL BE SAFE.

WELL, WELL... THE GENUINE DR. DANENBERG AT LAST.
I'M TERRIBLY SORRY ABOUT YOUR PARTNER, MR. CARDIGAN.

WHY'D YOU SEND AN ANDROID DUPE TO THAT MEETING?
I WAS AFRAID TO GO MYSELF.

I WAS CERTAIN THE TEK-LORDS WOULD TRY TO KILL ME!

YOU SEE, THE TEK CARTELS WANT ME DEAD BECAUSE OF MY PAST ASSOCIATION WITH LEON KITTRIDGE AND HIS DAUGHTER.
UNTIL A FEW MONTHS AGO, I HAD WORKED CLOSELY WITH THEM. I HAVE CONSIDERABLE KNOWLEDGE OF HIS ANTI-TEK SYSTEM.
IT INVOLVES USING HIGH-FREQUENCY OSCILLATION TO DESTROY EVERY TEK CHIP IN THE WORLD.
WOW.
DO YOU THINK THEY'VE KILLED THE KITTRIDGES?
OR DID HE AND BETH FAKE A CRASH AND GO INTO HIDING?
LEON AND I HAVEN'T BEEN CLOSE LATELY. I'M NOT CERTAIN OF HIS PLANS.
BUT I KNOW IT'S BEST FOR ME TO STAY IN HIDING.

SO WHY WERE YOU SO EAGER TO TALK TO ME?
BECAUSE I HAVE SOME INFORMATION THAT MAY HELP YOU.
THE KITTRIDGES HAVE A SECRET LAB HERE IN MEXICO. YOU MIGHT FIND OUT SOMETHING THERE.

INTERESTING. IS THE LAB NEAR HERE?
YES, NOT FAR. LEON CONVERTED AN OLD FACTORY IN THE JUNGLE.
HERE'S A MAP-- AND AN ELECTRO-KEY THAT'LL LET YOU IN.
AND SO...
THERE'S THE PLACE
AND NO SIGN OF AN AMBUSH.
NOBODY LURKING AROUND, EITHER.
SO LET'S HAVE A LOOK INSIDE.

LAB 1

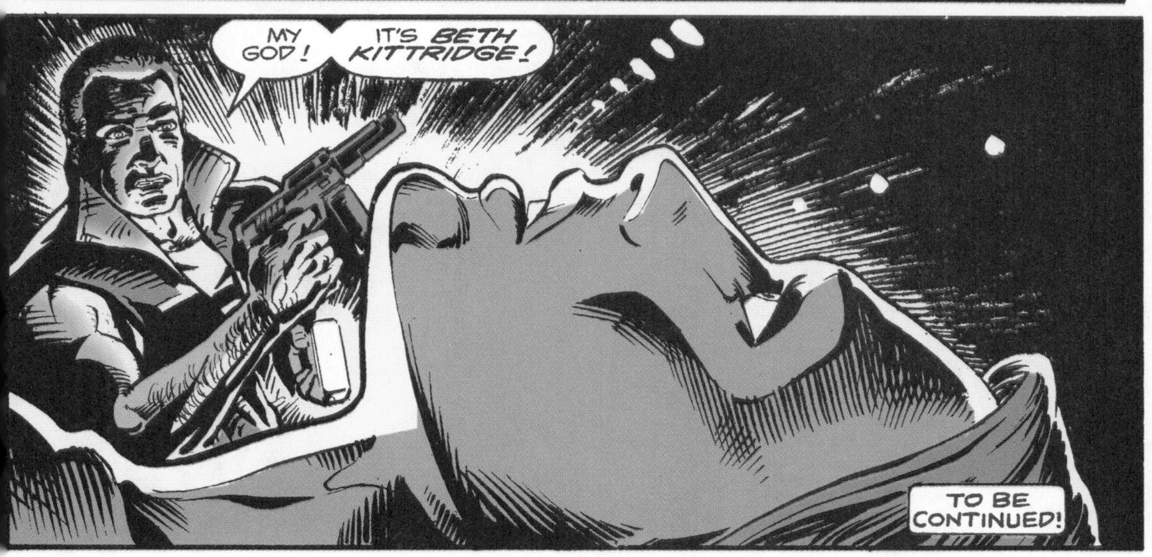
MY GOD!
IT'S *BETH KITTRIDGE!*
TO BE CONTINUED!

CHAPTER 3 WARBRIDE REVISITED

IN A HIDDEN LAB IN THE MEXICAN JUNGLE...
...JAKE CARDIGAN FINDS THE BODY OF A YOUNG WOMAN...
BETH KITTRIDGE--?!

WHOA -- IT'S ONLY AN ANDROID.
MAYBE ITS BRAIN KNOWS WHAT BETH'S DID!
IT'S ALREADY NEARLY COMPLETED.
IF I CAN FINISH IT UP, I CAN QUESTION IT.
LAB HAS ALL THE TOOLS I NEED.
CLEARVU
AFTER SEVERAL HOURS...
JUST ABOUT DONE.
I'M NO ELECTRONICS WHIZ, BUT--
YOU DID A PRETTY GOOD JOB...
EXCEPT YOU HOOKED THAT LAST YELLOW WIRE UP WRONG.

UM... I'M JAKE CARDIGAN, A DETECTIVE FROM THE COSMOS AGENCY-- FROM GREATER L.A.
THE KITTRIDGES HAVE VANISHED. SOMEWHERE IN MEXICO. I HAVE TO FIND THEM.
I'M BETH KITTRIDGE... WELL, YOU KNOW WHAT I MEAN.
A SIMULA-CRUM WITH ALL HER MEMORIES, FEELINGS AND SO ON.
I WAS BUILT TO TAKE HER PLACE IF THERE'S ANY DANGER.
OKAY, NOW I CAN GET DRESSED.
PROFESSOR KITTRIDGE FINISHED HIS ANTI-TEK SYSTEM.
THEY MUST HAVE RUSHED OFF TO ACAPULCO TO SHOW IT TO BENNETT SANDS.
SOME-THING MUST'VE HAPPENED TO THEM ON THE WAY.
YEAH, LOOKS LIKE THEY CRASHED SOMEPLACE IN THE GREAT FOREST.
JAKE--I'M GOING WITH YOU--HELP YOU LOCATE MY FATHER.
BRAPP
I WORK SOLO.

THAT ALARM MEANS THERE'RE INTRUDERS!
THEY'VE BROKEN INTO THE BUILDING-- THEY'RE HEADING THIS WAY!
TAKE A STUN-RIFLE.
AND ONE FOR ME.
KA-THWOUMM!
ARE YOU SURE YOU CAN HANDLE THAT--
STILL PREFER TO WORK ALONE, MR. CARDIGAN?

FZZZT
CABRON!
I OWE YOU ONE FOR THE HOTEL!
NOT JUST YET!
PHOON
COULD BE MORE OF 'EM ON THE WAY!
TIME TO RETREAT! C'MON, JAKE.
THIS'LL LEAD US TO A SPARE SKYCAR.
WE CAN USE ONE ABOUT NOW!
FZZZT
FZZZT
FZZT
C'MON!

I'LL FLY-- IF YOU DON'T MIND.
FINE-- THIS IS NO TIME TO ARGUE.
THAT DOOR WON'T HOLD 'EM FOR LONG!
LOOKS LIKE WE ARE GOING TO BE PARTNERS NOW, HUH?
YEAH-- FINE-- AT LEAST FOR NOW.

WE'VE GOT COMPANY
AND THEY'VE GOT A BIG SHIP.
VRRRRMMMM
NO WAY WE CAN OUTRUN THEM, JAKE-- SEE IF YOU CAN PICK THEM OFF!
YES, MA'AM.
VEEP
VEEP
THEY'RE CLOSING FAST!
ONLY CHANCE IS TO USE IT AGAINST THEM!

DIOS! WHERE'D THEY GO?
VWWWWRR
FWOOOSH
GREAT! I GOT 'EM SIGHTED!
FWACHOOMM
SEE? I KNEW WE'D MAKE A TERRIFIC TEAM!
MAYBE WE DO AT THAT.
WHERE TO NOW, JAKE?
LET'S HEAD FOR THE EDGE OF THE GREAT FOREST.
VRRRMMMM
THE NEXT MORNING...
OKAY, WELCOME TO CUIDADO, TOWN OF A THOUSAND SNORES.
IT'S NOT THE LEVEL OF EXCITEMENT I'M INTERESTED IN--
--IT'S THE PROXIMITY TO THE KITTRIDGES!

LATER THAT MORNING...
AN OLD FRIEND OF MINE IS WITH WARBRIDE'S FORCES...
...IF I CAN GET WORD TO HIM, HE'LL TAKE US TO HER CAMP.
OKAY, I'LL STAY HERE AS ORDERED.
IT'D BE SMARTER, THOUGH, TO LET ME GO ALONG.
SEVERAL CONVERSATIONS LATER...
I'M SURE, GLOBO.
I HEAR YOU CAN HELP ME CONTACT COLONEL RIBERA.
AH, BUENO! MI AMIGO.
I WAS JUST ABOUT TO CALL YOU, JAKE.
YOU DON'T NEED HIM. HER FRIEND VARGAS IS THE ONE TO RELY ON.
HE'S ARRANGING A GUIDE. TAKE YOU TO WARBRIDE.
WHERE DO I CONTACT THIS SOME-ONE?
PATIENCE, JAKE. I'LL TELL YOU EVERYTHING YOU NEED TO KNOW.

ARE YOU AN IDIOT, JAKE? GOING TO TOROS ELECTRICOS PLAZA--ALONE.
A MEETING IN THAT SHUT-DOWN AND RUN-DOWN PART OF TOWN SMELLS LIKE A TRAP!
IT COULD BE, BETH-- WHICH IS WHY YOU'RE SAFER AT HOME.
WELL, IF YOU INSIST ON BEING STUPID-- AT LEAST TRY TO BE CAREFUL.
I'LL TRY.
JUST HOPE THE PEOPLE I'M MEETING DO TOO...
SEÑOR! OVER HERE, POR FAVOR.
ARE YOU THE FRIEND OF WAR-BRIDE?
JAKE CARDIGAN.
GOOD-- THERE'S SOMEONE WAITING FOR YOU INSIDE.
I HAVE A KEY.
IS IT VARGAS HIM-SELF?
I DON'T KNOW HIS NAME.
BUT YOU'LL FIND HIM JUST THROUGH HERE...
ADIÓS, CABRÓN!

YOUR CONTACT IS HERE...
...BUT I DOUBT HE'LL TALK MUCH...
GREAT. BETH SURE WAS RIGHT--THIS WAS A SET-UP!
AND A PRETTY ELABORATE ONE--
--WHAT THE DEVIL IS THAT?
RRRROARRR
FSHOOM

MECHA-BULL! AND IT LOOKS LIKE I'M SUPPOSED TO PLAY--
--MATADOR!
TIME TO RETURN FIRE!
FOR ALL THE GOOD IT'LL DO AGAINST THAT MONSTER!

DIDN'T THINK SO.
THIS IS LOOKING PRETTY BAD...
REALLY BAD!

JAKE!!
VRRMMMM
HOP ABOARD!
SKRNCH
THOUGHT I TOLD YOU TO BE CAREFUL.
YOU TOLD ME TO *TRY*.
THIS *IS* ME TRYING.
GOOD THING I FOLLOWED YOU THEN...
...BY YOURSELF YOU JUST SEEM TO GET INTO ONE *MESS* AFTER ANOTHER.

LATER...
NO LUCK. NOBODY KNOWS WHERE GLOBO'S GOTTEN TO.
Cantina de Rosa
YOU THINK IT WAS VARGAS WHO HAD HIM SET YOU UP?
SOMEBODY HAD TO HAVE HIRED GLOBO--
HEY, JAKE!
I'VE BEEN LOOKING FOR YOU.
EDDIE RIBERA!
I MEAN COLONEL RIBERA.
I'VE GOT TO SEE WARBRIDE. CAN YOU FIX IT?
SURE, SI. ONCE SHE HEARD YOU WERE IN MEXICO--
--SHE SUGGESTED I FETCH YOU.
BE READY AT DAWN. I'LL PICK YOU UP AT YOUR INN.
SOMEBODY JUST TRIED TO KILL ME...
COULD VARGAS BE BEHIND THAT?
YOU CAN ASK HIM...
...WHEN YOU SEE HIM TOMORROW.

BY DUSK THEY'RE DEEP IN THE GREAT FOREST...
SHE HAS TO KNOW EVERY-THING THAT HAPPENS HERE-ABOUTS.
COULD SHE BE DIRECTLY INVOLVED?
I'D LIKE NOT TO THINK SO.
AND YOU DON'T KNOW ANYTHING ABOUT THE KITTRIDGE CRASH?
NADA, NO. IT'S POSSIBLE THAT WARBRIDE DOES.
LATER...
THE RALLY'S ALREADY STARTED, COLONEL.
I'VE HEARD THE SPEECH BEFORE.
YEAH, THAT'S WARBRIDE ALL RIGHT.
SHE REALLY DOESN'T SEEM YOUR TYPE, JAKE.

THERE IS NO ROOM AMONG US FOR ANYONE WHO IS NOT *LOYAL!*
IF YOU ARE AGAINST ME--YOU ARE AGAINST *MEXICO!*
IF YOU ARE AGAINST MEXICO-- **YOU MUST DIE!!**
I SAY AGAIN-- WE HAVE NO ROOM FOR *TRAITORS* AMONG US!
AND YET A TRAITOR HAS BEEN *FOUND!*
TONIGHT HE MUST *PAY* WITH HIS LIFE!

THIS IS THE WRETCH WHO BETRAYED ME!
GENERAL VARGAS HAS GIVEN ME PROOF OF IT!
THAT'S GLOBO!
HE BETRAYED ME-- NOT HER.
THEY'RE KILLING HIM TO KEEP HIM FROM TALKING!
SIT DOWN, JAKE. YOU CAN'T STOP HER NOW!
NEVER SAY, "YOU CAN'T," TO ME!

SOMEBODY WANTS TO SILENCE GLOBO.
BUT GLOBO ISN'T THE TRAITOR IN YOUR OUTFIT!
ELANA! LISTEN TO ME!
JAKE, DARLING--IT'S WONDERFUL TO SEE YOU AGAIN.
BUT, PLEASE--DON'T INTERFERE!
I WARN YOU, CARDIGAN!
KEEP OUT OF THIS!

GLOBO TRIED TO GET ME KILLED.
I THINK SOME-BODY IN YOUR CAMP ARRANGED IT!
I WOULD NEVER DO THAT, JAKE!
NO, BUT VARGAS WOULD--
AND NOW HE WANTS TO SHUT GLOBO UP FOR GOOD.
THERE'S NOTHING THAT FOOL CAN SAY THAT WOULD HURT ME!
HE COULD SAY YOU HIRED HIM.
MIGHT EVEN SAY THE TEK-LORDS WERE PAYING YOU.
THERE'S A SIMPLE WAY TO SETTLE THIS!
RAFE! WAIT!

MAYBE YOU NEED A ROBOT BULL TO HELP YOU, VARGAS!
NO I CAN HANDLE YOU MYSELF, GRINGO!
KRAK
ANOTHER TRAITOR!
GENERAL VARGAS WILL FIX HIM!
RAFE -- STOP --
VARGAS WILL SLAUGHTER HIM!
-- LEAVE HIM ALONE!
FSHMMM

THANKS-- ELANA-- FOR TAKING HIM DOWN--
NOW-- YOU'VE GOT TO STOP THIS EXECUTION.
WHICH EXECUTION WOULD THAT BE, JAKE?
GLOBO'S...
...OR YOURS--?
FSHMM
NEXT:
FATAL REUNION

CHAPTER 4 FATAL REUNION

FATAL REUNION
IN THE JUNGLES OF MEXICO, JAKE CARDIGAN INTERFERES IN AN EXECUTION--
--WHICH DOESN'T PLEASE WAR-BRIDE AT ALL.

HOURS LATER...
NOTHING'S WORSE THAN A STUNGUN HANGOVER.
GUESS IT DOESN'T PAY TO ARGUE WITH A WOMAN WHO HAS BUILT-IN WEAPONS.
BUT I STILL HAVE TO TALK TO HER...
ABOUT GETTING SAFE CONDUCT TO THE KITTRIDGE CRASH SITE.
OOPS!
CAN YOU TAKE ME TO WARBRIDE, POR FAVOR?
NO! YOU STAY HERE, SEÑOR!

I'D PREFER TO LEAVE NOW!
SWTHAK!
KRAK!
YOU DON'T NEED A GUN HERE, JAKE.
YOU'RE MY HONORED GUEST.
ELANA--!?

SORRY I HAD TO STUN YOU, CARIÑO.
BUT I DIDN'T WANT YOU AND RAFE KILLING EACH OTHER!
IT'S GOOD TO SEE YOU AGAIN!
AFTER SO MANY YEARS.
I'M NOT HERE TO RECAPTURE THE PAST, ELANA.
THE DETECTIVE AGENCY I WORK FOR NOW WANTS ME TO FIND PROFESSOR KITTRIDGE AND HIS DAUGHTER, BETH.
BUT ISN'T THE GIRL WITH YOU BETH?

"SHE'S AN ANDROID SIMULACRUM, WHO'S HELPING ME."
"THE REAL BETH AND HER DAD HAVE PERFECTED AN ANTI-TEK SYSTEM."
"LAST WEEK, WHILE FLYING OVER MEXICO..."
"THEY SUPPOSEDLY CRASHED NEAR HERE."
WHAT DO YOU KNOW ABOUT THEM?
NADA... NOTHING, JAKE.
BUT IT'S MY GUESS THEY'RE BOTH DEAD!

AND WHY DID YOU STOP GLOBO'S EXECUTION?
NOPE, THEY AREN'T DEAD.
IF THEY WERE, THERE WOULDN'T BE SO MANY PEOPLE TRYING TO STOP ME FROM FINDING THEM!
"SOMEBODY CONNED YOU ABOUT HIM. HE'S NOT A TRAITOR... NOT EXACTLY."
"GLOBO TRIED TO SET ME UP TO GET KNOCKED OFF."
"THE TEKLORDS WERE PROBABLY BEHIND THAT."
MEANING THAT GLOBO, VARGAS AND PROBABLY SOME OF YOUR OTHER PEOPLE--
--ARE LINKED WITH THE TEK TRADE.
NO, JAKE, THAT'S IM-POSSIBLE!

YOU KNOW THAT STUFF KILLED MY BROTHER!
MY PEOPLE AND I HAVE NOTHING TO DO WITH TEK--OR THE TEK CARTELS!

I THINK THE REAL REASON VARGAS WANTED GLOBO DEAD--
--WAS TO KEEP HIM FROM TALKING ABOUT HIS TEK CONNECTIONS!

NO ES VERDAD!
THAT'S A LIE!

WHY NOT JUST ASK VARGAS ABOUT IT?

WE'LL DO JUST THAT-- RIGHT NOW!
COME ALONG, JAKE!

QUERIDA-- WHAT THE HELL IS WRONG?
I WANT YOU TO TELL ME SOMETHING, RAFE!
DID YOU HAVE ANYTHING TO DO WITH THE PLANS TO KILL JAKE?
ARE YOU TAKING THE WORD OF THIS GRINGO-- FRESH OUT OF PRISON?
JUST ANSWER ME!
FOLKS, WHAT SAY WE GET GLOBO-- AND ASK HIM?

VERY WELL, I DID ORDER GLOBO TO ARRANGE CARDIGAN'S DEATH.
BUT THAT WAS ONLY BECAUSE I WAS JEALOUS.
IDIOTA! AND WHAT ABOUT THE KITTRIDGES?
SLAM!
I WANT THE TRUTH! ALL OF IT!
ALL RIGHT, YES... THEY DIDN'T CRASH.
I HAD THEIR SKY-CRUISER FORCED DOWN NEAR HERE.

HEY, ELANA-- HOLD OFF!
TELL US WHAT HAPPENED THEN, VARGAS.
SONNY HOKORI'S MEN CAME FOR THEM.
THEY TOOK THEM TO ACAPULCO.
RAFE-- HOKORI IS A TOP TEK KINGPIN!
LISTEN, WE ALWAYS NEED MONEY.
SO I DECIDED TO DEAL WITH TEKLORDS BEHIND YOUR BACK.
I LOVED YOU, RAFE--
RZZT
--BUT NOBODY DISOBEYS ME!
ELANA, DON'T!

EARLY THE NEXT MORNING...
HASTA LA VISTA, JAKE. AND BE VERY CAREFUL!
I INTEND TO-- AND THANKS FOR THE LOAN OF THE SKYCAR.
WELL?
WELL, WHAT?
DID YOU SPEND THE NIGHT WITH THAT WOMAN?
MATTER OF FACT, BETH-- I DID...
...BUT NOT IN THE WAY YOU MEAN.

EN ROUTE JAKE FILLS BETH IN ON WHAT HE'S LEARNED AND WHAT HE HOPES TO FIND IN ACAPULCO...
THE MORE I THINK ABOUT THIS, JAKE--
--THE MORE I WONDER IF MY FATHER MIGHT HAVE SOLD OUT TO THE TEK CARTELS.
I ALMOST WISH I COULD GET AWAY BY MYSELF.
MY UNCLE HAS A PLACE ON THE MOON COLONY THAT'S PERFECT FOR SITTING AND THINKING.
THERE'S OUR HOTEL, BETH.
RIGHT... BACK TO REALITY.
Acapulco
Acapulco

HERE'S YOUR GREATER L.A. CALL, SEÑOR.
HI, JAKE!
GOMEZ! YOU'RE BACK ON THE JOB?
RITZ
ROOFTOP RECEPTIO
SI. AND THE MEDICS SAY I CAN JOIN YOU DOWN THERE SOON.
MEANTIME, I'VE BEEN GATHERING THE INFO YOU ASKED FOR.
FIRST, THOUGH, YOUR ERSTWHILE SPOUSE HAS BEEN TRYING TO REACH YOU.
KATE? IS MY SON OKAY?
"THE LADY DIDN'T SAY."
"ONLY THAT IT'S URGENT!"
SO I TOLD HER WHAT HOTEL YOU'RE AT... IS THAT ALL RIGHT?
SURE, SID.

AS FOR INFORMANTS DOWN YOUR WAY... THE MOST RELIABLE ONE IN OUR FILES IS A LAD CALLED *FAXIMO.*
HE LOOKS LIKE THIS AND HANGS OUT IN AN OFFICE IN BACK OF MAMA YMA'S CAFE. HE'S *NEARLY* 75% HONEST.

THANKS, SID. KEEP ON RECUPERAT-ING.
YOU TOO, *AMIGO*.
IF YOU FIND OUT WHAT KATE WANTS, LET ME KNOW.

YOU *SURE* YOU DON'T WANT ME TO GO ALONG?
NOT ON THIS INITIAL RUN, NO.
I'D LIKE YOU TO STAY IN OUR SUITE AND WATCH THE PHONE.
OKAY-- TAKE CARE.
FIRST TIME YOU'VE EVER BEEN KISSED BY A MACHINE?
YEAH, I GUESS IT IS.

TEN MINUTES LATER...
Café
MAMA YMA
I HEAR YOU'RE INTERESTED IN SONNY HOKORI. HE'S STILL IN ACAPULCO...
HOKORI SONNY
...AND HOLED UP AT HIS PLEASURE DOME, AN EXTREMELY POSH CASINO-RESORT.
WHAT ABOUT BENNETT SANDS?
HE, TOO, IS IN TOWN, RESIDING IN YONDER VILLA.
BUT COME BACK AT NINE TONIGHT. I'LL HAVE SOMETHING BY THEN.
NO NEWS ON THE KITTRIDGES EITHER.
BE EXTREMELY WATCHFUL, MY FRIEND.
I ALSO HEAR THERE ARE PEOPLE HERE-ABOUTS WHO WANT YOU DEAD--GRAVE-YARD DEAD.

AS JAKE HEADS BACK TO THE HOTEL...
THAT'S HIM, JEFE! THAT'S THE GUY.
HEY, SEÑOR CARDIGAN!
WOULD YOU MIND TAKING A LITTLE WALK WITH US? SOMEBODY WANTS TO SEE YOU.
KRAK
SINCE YOU ASK--
--YEAH-- I WOULD MIND!
QUICK-- GET HIM!
BUT DON'T KNOCK HIM OUT.
GOTCHA, JEFE.

THERE! THAT *STOPPED* HIM!
I HOPE YOUR LAZ-GUN'S ON THE *RIGHT* SETTING!

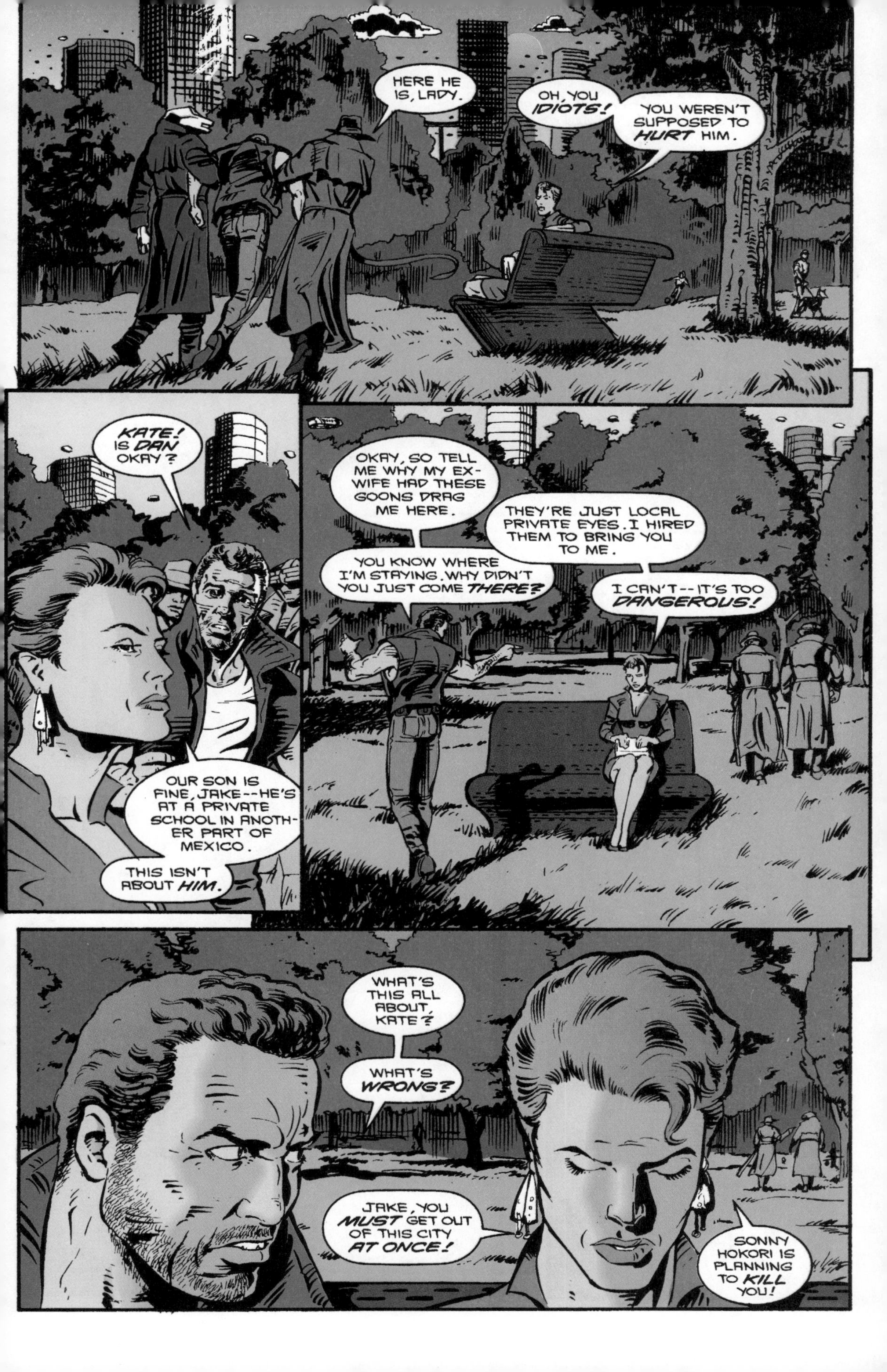
HERE HE IS, LADY.
OH, YOU IDIOTS!
YOU WEREN'T SUPPOSED TO HURT HIM.
KATE! IS DAN OKAY?
OUR SON IS FINE, JAKE--HE'S AT A PRIVATE SCHOOL IN ANOTHER PART OF MEXICO.
THIS ISN'T ABOUT HIM.
OKAY, SO TELL ME WHY MY EX-WIFE HAD THESE GOONS DRAG ME HERE.
THEY'RE JUST LOCAL PRIVATE EYES. I HIRED THEM TO BRING YOU TO ME.
YOU KNOW WHERE I'M STAYING. WHY DIDN'T YOU JUST COME THERE?
I CAN'T--IT'S TOO DANGEROUS!
WHAT'S THIS ALL ABOUT, KATE?
WHAT'S WRONG?
JAKE, YOU MUST GET OUT OF THIS CITY AT ONCE!
SONNY HOKORI IS PLANNING TO KILL YOU!

HOW DO YOU KNOW THAT?
STILL A COP AT HEART...CAN'T STOP ASKING QUESTIONS.
JUST TELL ME HOW YOU FOUND OUT.
I CAN'T... BUT TRUST ME. YOU'RE NOT SAFE IN ACAPULCO.

I HAVE TO LEAVE. IT'S RISKY TO STAY TOO LONG.
ARE YOU LIVING WITH SANDS?
YES, JAKE.
YES, I AM.

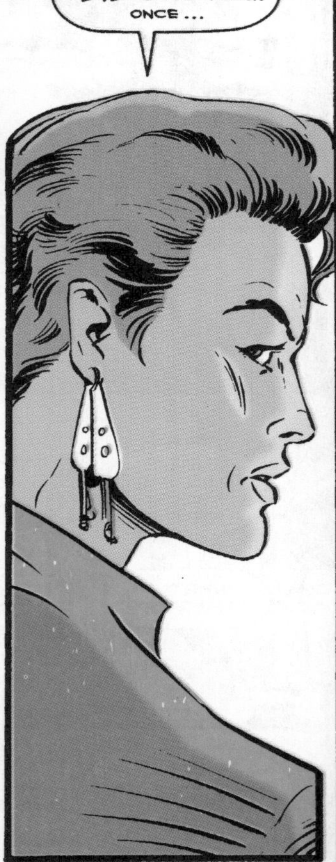
I'M SORRY THINGS TURNED OUT THIS WAY FOR US.
I REALLY DID LOVE YOU... ONCE...

LATER THAT NIGHT...
Acapulco
RITZ RITZ
I'VE BEEN OUT OF THE FREEZER FOR A WHILE NOW, BETH...
BUT I'M JUST STARTING TO WAKE UP.
ABOUT YOUR WIFE, YOU MEAN?
FORMER WIFE. SANDS HAS TO BE TIED IN WITH SONNY HOKORI.
I'M WONDERING IF KATE KNEW ABOUT MY FRAME-UP IN ADVANCE.
IT'S ROUGH WHEN YOU CAN'T TRUST SOMEONE YOU LOVE.
IT IS, YEAH.

YOU DO SEEM TO BE GETTING SMARTER, JAKE.
HOW SO?
WELL, YOU'RE LETTING ME COME ALONG TO THIS MEETING WITH FAXIMO.
I MAY NEED YOUR HELP BEFORE THE NIGHT'S OVER.

HEY! LOOK UP AHEAD!
IT'S DAN!

HI, DAD!
ELEVATOR W34
I CUT SCHOOL TO BE WITH YOU!

JAKE, WAIT!
YOU DON'T UNDERSTAND-- IT'S MY SON!

NO, JAKE!
DON'T GO NEAR HIM!
DAD? WHAT'S SHE DOING?
BETH?
MY GOD!
DAN!
NEXT:
TEK WAR

CHAPTER 5
TEK WAR

TEK WAR
THEY WERE ON A PEDESTRIAN RAMP IN ACAPULCO.
IT WAS THE FIRST TIME JAKE CARDIGAN HAD SEEN HIS SON, DAN, IN YEARS. THE REUNION HAS BEEN BRIEF, TO SAY THE LEAST...
GOOD GOD, BETH!
WHAT ARE YOU DOING?!

NOOO!
IT WAS A KAMIKAZE ANDROID--
--BETH SENSED THAT.
THAT WASN'T DAN!
SHE SACRIFICED HERSELF.
FOR ME.

Acapulco

WHY SO SAD, SEÑOR?
LET ME CHEER YOU UP!

IF I FIND A TEK PARLOR... I CAN FORGET ALL THIS FOR AWHILE.
HEY, HOMBRE--OVER HERE!
I GOT WHAT YOU NEED!
YOU LOOK LIKE YOU NEED TO ESCAPE FROM YOUR TROUBLES, AMIGO.
BRAZIL VET
I GOT GAMBLING, BOOZE, WOMEN--
NOT INTERESTED.
BRAZIL VET
HOW ABOUT THE BEST ESCAPE OF THEM ALL... TEK?
NO! IT WOULD BE TOO EASY.
THERE'S SOMETHING I HAVE TO TAKE CARE OF FIRST!

LATER, IN A MUCH NICER SECTION OF ACAPULCO.
IN THE HOME OF BENNETT SANDS...
CLICK
HUHM... JAKE?!
YOU FOOL!
GET OUT OF HERE BEFORE IT'S TOO LATE!
IT'S ALREADY TOO LATE, KATE.
FOR A LOT OF THINGS.

YOUR LAZGUN'S NOT THERE, SANDS. IT'S HERE.
HOW'D YOU GET BY MY SECURITY SYSTEM?
I'M AN EXPERT AT THAT SORT OF THING. I USED TO BE A COP BEFORE I GOT FRAMED.
I'LL MAKE A LOAD OF TROUBLE FOR YOU, CARDIGAN!
YOU'LL HAVE TO BE ALIVE TO TRY THAT...
...AND UNLESS YOU DO EXACTLY WHAT I TELL YOU--
--YOU WON'T BE!

YOU'RE NOT GIVING *ME* ORDERS!
KRUNCH
THWUMPH
KRAK
KATE--THE GUN!!
KILL HIM!
C'MON, SANDS-- TAKE ME TO *SONNY HOKORI'S* PLACE.
AND KEEP IN MIND-- I'M REAL *CLOSE* TO LOSING MY PATIENCE.

THIRTY MINUTES LATER...
Welcome TO THE PLEASURE DOME
WHY COME HERE, CARDIGAN?
BECAUSE THIS IS WHERE THE KITTRIDGES ARE.
IT'S SUICIDE GOING UP AGAINST HOKORI ON HIS OWN TERRITORY!
IT'LL BE SUICIDE FOR YOU IF ANYBODY TRIES TO STOP US.
THIS GENTLEMAN IS WITH ME, RUDY.
SO BE VERY CONVINCING.
YES SIR, MR. SANDS.
YOU OUGHT TO STOP FOR A DRINK, CARDIGAN.
IT'LL BE YOUR LAST!

IT'S OKAY, TUX. HE'S WITH ME.
MANAGER
HEY--CARDIGAN! GOOD TA SEE YA!

LET'S TALK, SONNY.
ARE YA PEEVED 'CAUSE I FRAMED YA? YOU KNOW, THAT WAS STRICTLY BUSINESS.

APOLOGY ACCEPTED-- NOW TAKE ME TO KITTRIDGE AND HIS DAUGHTER!
I TOLD HIM HE WAS CRAZY, SONNY.
SURE, YA GOT THIS ALL WRONG, JAKE, BUDDY.
HAVEN'T ANY IDEA WHERE THEY ARE!

I RAN OUT OF PATIENCE FOUR YEARS AGO!
BRING THEM TO THIS OFFICE NOW! OR I START USING THIS LAZGUN.
WELL, I MIGHT BE ABLE TO ROUND UP THE PROF FOR YA.
BUT THE DAME IS SOMETHIN' ELSE AGAIN.
YA SEE, SHE-- HEY!
ICCA
IT'S A RAID!

IDCA
WINTERGUILD--?!
FWAS

IDCA
YOU HALF-WIT! YOU KILLED HOKORI JUST AS HE WAS GOING TO --
THIS IS AN OFFICIAL INTERNATIONAL DRUG CONTROL AGENCY RAID.
JUST KEEP OUT OF MY WAY!
WHILE YOU GENTLEMEN ARE ARGUING, I'LL BORROW THIS!
NOW--STAY BACK. I'M MAKING MY EXIT.

GOOD WORK, *WEBER!*

SEE, CARDIGAN? WE HANDLED THE SITUATION!

YEAH, IN YOUR USUAL SUBTLE WAY.

BETH WAS--
--ABLE TO GET AWAY--
--SHE ESCAPED--
--TWO DAYS AGO.
THEN WHERE IS SHE? WHY DIDN'T SHE GO TO THE COPS?
SHE'S PROBABLY--
--IN HIDING--
--I FEAR SHE DOESN'T--
--QUITE TRUST ME OR...
HE'S PASSED OUT.
DON'T WORRY--WE'LL FIND THE GIRL. THAT'S OUR JOB.
IDCA

WHY DID YOU PULL SUCH A DESTRUCTIVE RAID?
RELAX, MY BOY. WE GOT THE RESULTS WE WANTED.
I TOLD YOU I WAS GOING TO HANDLE THIS MESS MY WAY.
WHICH REMINDS ME--
KRAK
--THAT'S THE ONE I PROMISED YOU BACK IN GREATER L.A.

EARLY NEXT MORNING...
WINGER--? WHAT ARE YOU DOING HERE?
THE SOCAL PAROLE BOARD SENT ME.
GO AWAY--I'M FINISHING UP A JOB.
YOU'VE VIOLATED YOUR PAROLE.
I'M ESCORTING YOU HOME FOR A HEARING.
I DON'T HAVE TIME FOR THAT NOW!
AH, BUT YOU DO, CARDIGAN.
LOOK-- I THINK I KNOW WHERE BETH KITTRIDGE IS.
BE THAT AS IT MAY, YOU--
AWK!

AMAZING WHAT ONE LITTLE TASER CAN DO, ISN'T IT?
SID GOMEZ?! YOU RECUPERATED JUST IN THE NICK OF TIME.
SI, I'M IN TIPTOP SHAPE-- SO COSMOS SENT ME TO HELP OUT.
GREAT! RIGHT NOW WE HAVE TO GET OURSELVES TO THE MOON COLONY--FAST!
I'M PRETTY SURE BETH KITTRIDGE IS THERE.
WHY, AMIGO?
SEE, THE BETH ANDROID TOLD ME ABOUT A HIDE-AWAY THE REAL BETH MIGHT USE.
YOU DON'T HAVE ANY PROOF, THOUGH?
NOPE, BUT I'VE GOT ONE HECK OF A HUNCH!

WE HAVE TO AVOID THE REGULAR SPACEPORTS, JAKE.
SORT OF A... COUSIN OF MINE. VERY RELIABLE.
WHO RUNS THIS PRIVATE SET-UP?
MONTANYA
NOVELTY Co
RELIABLE'S NOT A WORD I ASSOCIATE WITH MANY OF YOUR KIN.
MONTANYA'S DIFFERENT. HE'S HARDLY EVER EVEN BEEN IN JAIL.
OH, AND TRY NOT TO MAKE ANY NASTY RE-MARKS ABOUT THE SHIP HE'S LENDING US.
SID, YOU'RE EXPECTING TO GET TO THE MOON IN THIS... ANTIQUE?
THINK OF IT AS A CLASSIC, AMIGO. THEY BUILT 'EM TO LAST IN THOSE DAYS.
MI PRIMO! EVERYTHING LOOKS SHIP-SHAPE TO ME.

SEE, AMIGO? A PERFECT LAUNCH.
CAN'T HEAR YOU WITH ALL THIS RATTLING, SID...
LATER...
WE MADE IT, JAKE. A SMOOTH AND UNEVENTFUL JAUNT.
WELL, UNEVENTFUL ANYWAY.

AND THAT'S WHY YOU'RE SO EAGER TO FIND THE TRUE MISS KITTRIDGE?
WE WERE HIRED TO FIND HER, REMEMBER?
YOU'RE NOT ESPECIALLY CHEERFUL, JAKE.
I LIKED BETH--THE BETH ANDROID, ANYWAY...
...I REALLY MISS HER.

CLEAR
MONORAIL TERMINAL
SECURITY
BUT, YEAH... I SUPPOSE THERE IS A PERSONAL ANGLE NOW.

THIS'LL TAKE US TO THE OLD MANSION WHERE I THINK SHE'S STAYING.
FOR YOUR SAKE, I HOPE THE LADY'S AT HOME.

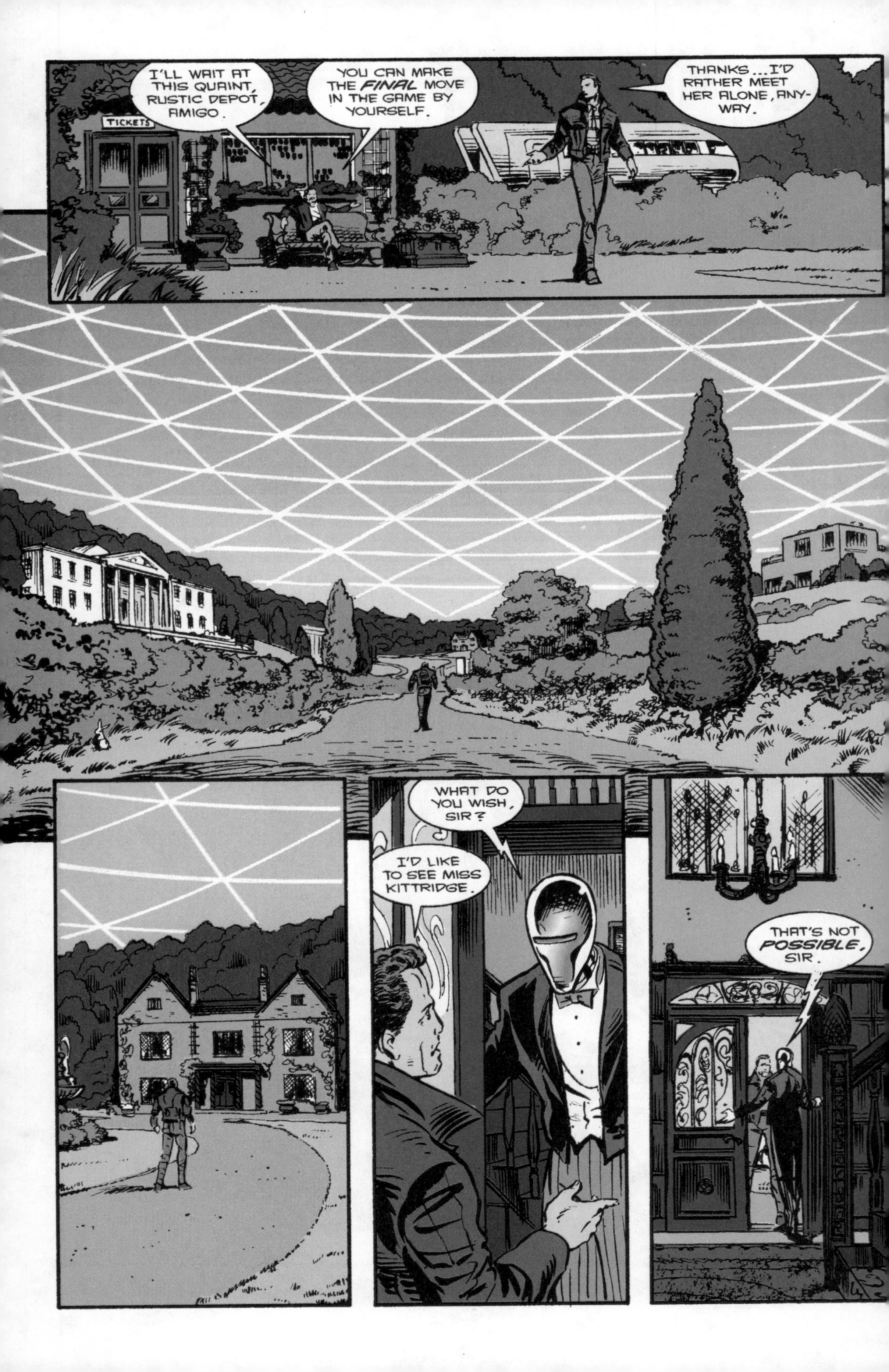
I'LL WAIT AT THIS QUAINT, RUSTIC DEPOT, AMIGO.
YOU CAN MAKE THE *FINAL* MOVE IN THE GAME BY YOURSELF.
THANKS...I'D RATHER MEET HER ALONE, ANY-WAY.
TICKETS
WHAT DO YOU WISH, SIR?
I'D LIKE TO SEE MISS KITTRIDGE.
THAT'S NOT *POSSIBLE*, SIR.

MAKE IT POSSIBLE.
NAME'S CARDIGAN. WITH THE COSMOS DETECTIVE AGENCY.

I'VE GOT TO SEE HER. NOW.
WAIT! YOU CAN'T COME IN!
MISS KITTRIDGE!

IT'S ALL RIGHT, EDWARD. I'LL TALK TO HIM.

PLEASE, EXPLAIN WHY YOU'RE HERE AND WHAT YOU WANT.
OR I WILL SHOOT YOU DOWN COLD.
I'M JAKE CARDIGAN.
I WAS HIRED TO FIND YOU-- TO PROTECT YOU
HOKORI'S DEAD-- AND YOUR FATHER IS SAFE.
IT'S OKAY TO COME HOME NOW.
YOU SEEM LIKE SOMEONE I CAN TRUST.
I AM, YEAH.
BUT MAYBE YOU NEED SOME TIME TO THINK.
HOLD ON, JAKE. DON'T GO.
IT'S FUNNY--BUT I FEEL WE'VE MET SOME-PLACE BE-FORE.
IN A WAY, WE HAVE.
LET ME TELL YOU ABOUT IT...

AFTERWORD

AFTERWORD

William Shatner with Greg Evigan, who plays Jake Cardigan in the TEK movie. Shatner plays Walt Bascom Head of Cosmos Security.

The future is in good hands.

That was the reassuring message I always received as I watched Captain Kirk and his stalwart crew save the known universe every night in full color. Yes, let's get it out in the open, right off the bat: my name is Evan Skolnick, and I am a recovering Trekaholic.

"So what?" I hear you thinking. (I can do that, by the way.) "Join the club. . .in fact, join any of the hundreds of clubs." You're thinking I'm like every other Trekker — big deal. And you're right, except for one thing.

I got to meet William Shatner.

The first time was in the summer of 1992, at Planet Hollywood here in New York. The very first TEKWORLD comic book, based on Mr. Shatner's bestselling book series, was about to hit the stands. Marvel was lucky enough to set up a press conference in time to help promote the comic book, and Mr. Shatner was kind enough to agree to speak during the press conference. Carlos Lopez (the TEKWORLD assistant editor) and I (the lowly colorist) were on hand, basking in the electrically-charged atmosphere that a star always creates — and hoping against hope that we'd get a chance to meet the man himself.

Meanwhile, Mr. Shatner (at least eight feel tall. . .easy) gave his presentation before the assembled journalists, telling them how bemused he was to see himself translated into the comics medium — although there's a 'coincidental' resemblance between the comic book Jake Cardigan and the real-life William Shatner, only one of them is built like a super hero*! Mr. Shatner also made a pointed effort to describe the comic book creation process, graciously crediting Ron Goulart, Lee Sullivan, Pat Brosseau and (gasp!) even me with our respective tasks and talents. Oh yeah, and Fabian, too.*

Then came the moment of truth. . .we were allowed "backstage" after the presentation to meet William Shatner! I won't go into the gory details, partially for space considerations and partially because I don't want to further embarrass Carlos. (Let's just say that Mr. Shatner seemed somewhat more intrigued with the computer coloring process than the assistant editing process.)

The second time was much more recent, and much more intense. Ultra-talented TEKWORLD artist Lee Sullivan was planning a transatlantic journey to Marvel's New York headquarters (he's English, don't you know), with a side-trip to Toronto to visit the set of the first Tek made-for-TV movie, Tekwar*! A few weeks earlier, I had been hired as TEKWORLD's new writer, and since Lee and I go way back to the days when he was the beleaguered ROBOCOP penciler and I was the beleaguered ROBOCOP assistant editor, we decided —*

Okay, time out. Now *you're thinking that Fabian must be crazy, hiring a colorist to be a writer. Well, thanks a lot, that's real nice. Just to set the record straight, Fabian* is *crazy, but that had nothing to do with his decision to hire me to write TEKWORLD starting in January 1994. I can only assume that it was my previous writing on Marvel titles such as DEATHLOK, ROBOCOP, EXCALIBUR and 2099 UNLIMITED which convinced him. Then again, it might have been those photos I took at his bachelor party. . .*

Greg Evigan and Torri Higginson. Torri portrays Beth Kittridge, Jake's love interest in the televison adaptation of the novel.

Anyway, you can see where this is headed: Toronto. The set of Tekwar. *The pictures speak for themselves; this is going to be one hot movie series. But there are some things the photos* can't *tell you. Here they are:*

1. Toronto is a great place. You really ought to go there sometime, even if you're not visiting a movie set.

2. Directors are not *the busiest people on the set, like you'd think they'd be. Mr. Shatner (did I mention he's directing* Tekwar, *the first of the movie series, as well as acting in it?) was often busy waiting for everyone else to do their thing — very efficiently, mind you — so that he could do his. He therefore had a lot more time on his hands than you'd expect to spend with annoying hangers-on like myself. (Sorry, Lee, I couldn't include you there because I can't say anything nasty about you — you're just too damn nice.) Which he did spend, most freely and generously.*

Jake and Beth accompanied by Jake's parole officer, Winger (played by actor Maurice Dean Wint), soon after Jake's release from the Freezer

3. Call him "Bill." Everyone does — really. And that's not all. Every member of the cast and crew loves him. Loves him. *Why? I dunno. I suppose it could be the fact that he is universally patient, energetic, fun, and kind to everybody he's working with. I don't care what you might have heard or read in other places. . .this is the real deal.*

4. People who work in the movies will make the mistake of thinking you're some kind of celebrity if you work in comics. It's the most amazing thing. Lee and I ended up autographing stuff for Greg Evigan who's playing Jake Cardigan in the series — go figure!

5. People who work in the movies — at least these *movies — are also incredibly friendly and fun. The atmosphere at Cardigan Productions (great name, eh?) was professional but always light, and we were treated like everybody's new pals. I wish I had the space to really go into this, but my wife might read this someday. (Ha ha, honey — just kidding! No, really!)*

6. A lifetime Trekker, under the right circumstances, can completely conceal his malady for professional reasons — even if he were to suddenly realize that he was having dinner at a Thai restaurant with Captain Kirk. (Well, almost completely.)

It was quite an adventure. Lee and I hope to go back before the fourth movie, Teklab, *is finished shooting — to experience that creative vortex once again, a synergy of talent, troubleshooting and teamwork all revolving around one man's stark, harrowing vision of the future.*

Like I said, with William Shatner and TEK World, the future is in good hands.

Jake and Beth confront a dying cyborg.

Evan Skolnick
October 1993

William Shatner's TEKWORLD is the hard-hitting Marvel/Epic comic book series based on the actor/director's acclaimed science fiction novels. In 1994 — just in time for the release of the Tek TV movies — TEKWORLD shifts into high gear, with a brash new writer, a futuristic new art style, startling new characters and pulse-pounding new stories! Experience the future as only William Shatner could imagine it!

LEE
SULLIVAN

A NEW TEK WORLD ADVENTURE IS IN THE CARDS

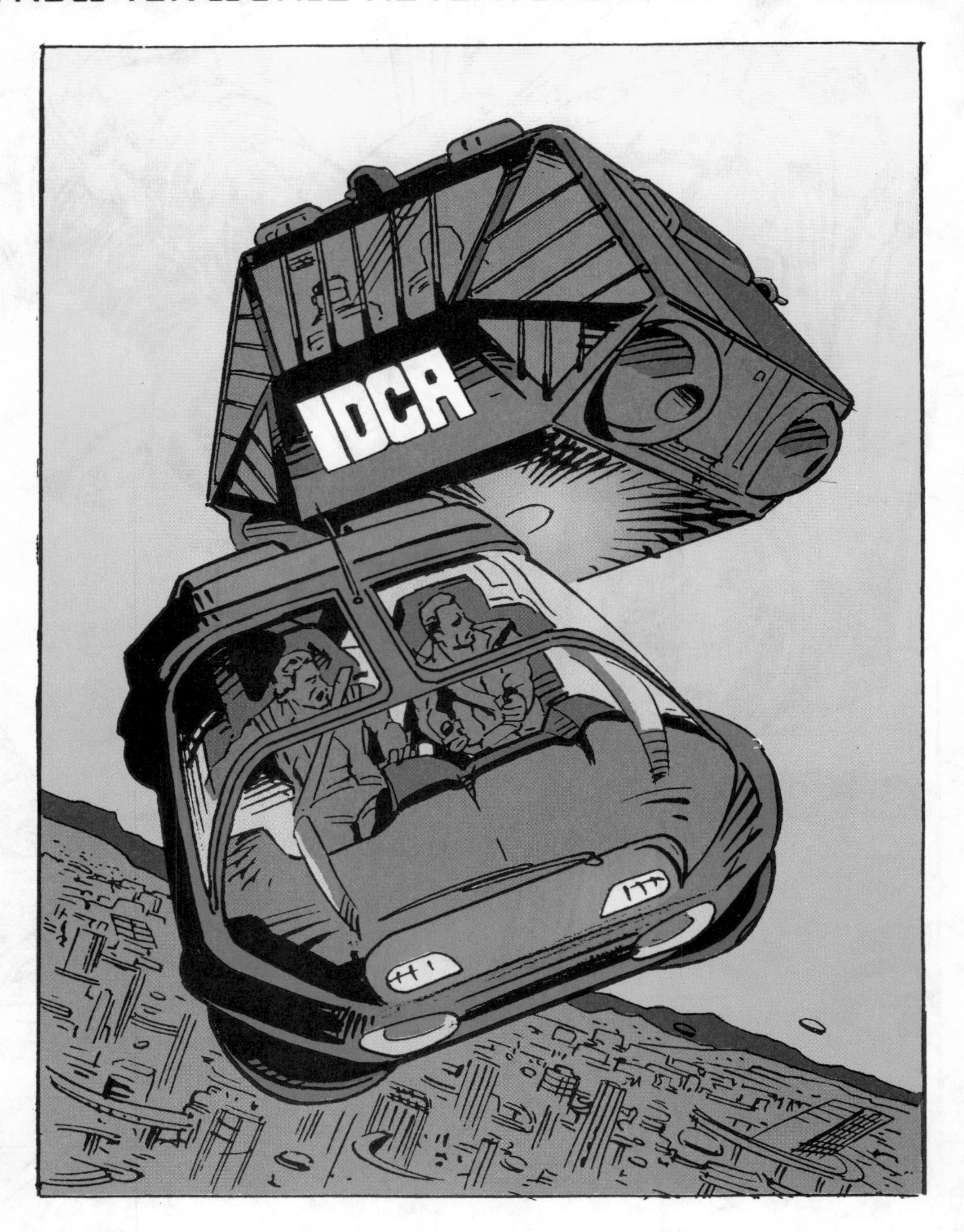

The futuristic world created by actor, director, producer, turned writer, William Shatner, is featured in a new trading car series from CARDZ Distribution. TEK World was introduced as a series of best selling novels and has evolved into fou made-for- televesion movies and a popular comic book series. The trading card series will feature well-known TEK Worl characters in an entirely new story which is revealed in the cards.

William Shatner's TEK World trading cards consist of a 100-card set which features eight-card, foil-wrapped packs wit a suggested retail price of $1.49 each.

Much like the comic book, the story of TEK World trading cards involves a journey into the future where humans battle laser-toting cyborgs, cities have become war zones and "virtual reality," a computer-generated state of animation, is the "drug of choice."

Creator of the TEK World saga, William Shatner adds, "These cards capture the energy of the TEKWAR world. I think anyone who has been following the TEK World series will want to collect the entire set!"